Contents

Dear Learner:

This little workbook is here to give you extra practice with short-vowel words. Turn to it each time you complete a new title. Answering the comprehension questions and doing the activities will help you become a super-strong reader, writer, and speller.

Happy Learning!

Your Friends at Scholastic

Comprehension Questions

NOTE TO CAREGIVER: After your child reads a book, invite him/her to answer the three comprehension questions. To extend learning, challenge your child to create original story-related questions to ask you!

Sam's Cat Jan (short a)

1. What things made Jan mad?
2. Did Jan like her new pal? How do you know?
3. Can you think of three or more words to describe Jan?

Jen Pen (short e)

1. Can you remember all of the things Jen Pen drew? Give it a try.
2. What happens at the end of the story?
3. What things do you like to draw? Talk about it.

Kim Is It! (short i)

1. What game are Kim and Pig playing?
2. What places were not good hiding places for Pig? What place was a good hiding place for Pig?
3. What games do you like to play with your pals? Talk about it.

Log Hop (short o)

1. Who was the first animal to get on the log?
2. Why did the animals fall off the log?
3. How did Pop save the day?

Cub and Pug (short u)

1. Who are the two characters in this story?
2. How do Cub and Pug get dirty? How do Cub and Pug get clean?
3. Would you like to play with Cub and Pug? Talk about it.

Red Hen's Bus (short vowels)

1. What made Cub, Pig, and Ox sad?
   (TIP: Look at the pictures for clues.)
2. What made Cub, Pig, and Ox happy?
3. What makes you happy when you are sad? Talk about it.

Mel Did Not Say "Yum!" (short vowels)

1. What things did Mom put in the cup of mud for Mel?
2. Did Mel like the cup of mud? How do you know?
3. What is your favorite food? Talk about it.

Cam and Pat (short vowels)

1. Why did Pat want to see Cam?
2. What problems happened when Pat went to see Cam?
3. How did Pat solve his last problem and get to see Cam?

Zig and Zag (short vowels)

1. What fun things did Zig and Zag do?

2. Why do Zig and Zag go up? Why do Zig and Zag go down?

3. Would you like to play with Zig and Zag? Talk about it.

Gus Can Get a Pet (short vowels)

1. Where do Gus and his dad go to find a pet?

2. Which animals does Dad say are not pets? Do you agree? Why?

3. At the end of the story, what pet does Gus get? Why is this silly?

Ben Bat Is Sad (short vowels)

1. Why is it hard for Ben Bat to make a pal?

2. Who does become Ben Bat's pal?

3. How are Ben Bat and the big bug alike and different?

Dot's Big Red Hat (short vowels)

1. What happens when Dot says the magic words "DAB-DIB-A-DUB?"

2. What happens at the end of the story?

3. Would you like to have a magic hat like Dot does? Talk about it.

Short-Vowel Sound Review 1

NOTE TO CAREGIVER: Challenge your child to read each word and match it to the right picture. TIP: If he/she struggles, review short-vowel sounds.

cub

pig

dog

cat

pen

Short-Vowel Sound Review 2

NOTE TO CAREGIVER: Challenge your child to read each word and match it to the right picture. TIP: If he/she struggles, review short-vowel sounds.

     fox

     bus

     fan

     hen

     bib

Sam's Cat Jan

Review the sound.

short *a*		cat

Circle the words.

cat mad fan jam nap

b r f a n z e j a m
q b o r c a t i q l
n a p f o s m a d u

Practice
Read, trace, and write the words.

cat cat

mad mad

fan fan

jam jam

nap nap

Jen Pen

Review the sound.

short e		pen

Circle the words.

pen   red   web   bed   jet

p e n m z j e t r o
x b e d l a t u f g
y a r e d l h w e b

Practice

Read, trace, and write the words.

pen   pen

red   red

bed   bed

web   web

jet   jet

Kim Is It!

Review the sound.

short *i*		pig

Circle the words.

pig   kid   did   fit   wig

```
t k i d b a x r n r
p i g m l o s d i d
e w i g y f i t u z
```

Practice
Read, trace, and write the words.

pig   pig

kid   kid

did   did

fit   fit

wig   wig

Log Hop

Review the sound.

short o		dog

Circle the words.

dog   hop   fox   top   not

g f o x h j a t o p
n o t m q a d o g k
y u h o p l h d i z

Practice

Read, trace, and write the words.

dog   dog

hop   hop

fox   fox

top   top

not   not

Cub and Pug

Review the sound.

short *u*		cub

Circle the words.

cub	pug	sun	mud	tub

p u g n c j u l p o
z s u n l i t u b q
d m u d k e x c u b

Practice
Read, trace, and write the words.

cub   cub

pug   pug

sun   sun

mud   mud

tub   tub

Red Hen's Bus

Review the sounds.

short *a*	short *e*	short *i*	short *o*	short *u*

sad	hen	fix	ox	bus

Circle the words.

| sad | hen | fix | ox | bus |

o x g n s a d l g a

z k j b u s e v w t

h e n g k v y f i x

Practice
Read, trace, and write the words.

sad　sad

hen　hen

fix　fix

ox　ox

bus　bus

Mel Did Not Say "Yum!"

Review the sounds.

short *a*	short *e*	short *i*	short *o*	short *u*
JAM	RED	bib	pot	cup
jam	red	bib	pot	cup

Circle the words.

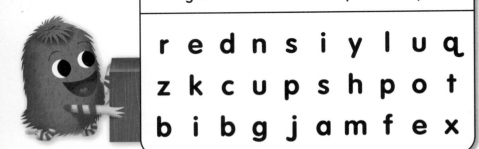

jam   red   bib   pot   cup

```
r e d n s i y l u q
z k c u p s h p o t
b i b g j a m f e x
```

Practice
Read, trace, and write the words.

jam jam

red red

bib bib

pot pot

cup cup

Cam and Pat

Review the sounds.

short *a*	short *e*	short *i*	short *o*	short *u*
ram	ten	jig	top	up

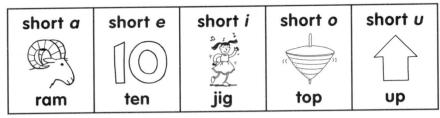

Circle the words.

ram   ten   jig   top   up

```
c t e n s t d j i g
z k w p a g t o p r
s r a m k y u p e x
```

Laugh-a-Lot Phonics: Short Vowels © Scholastic Inc.

Practice
Read, trace, and write the words.

ram ram

ten ten

jig jig

top top

up up

Zig and Zag

Review the sounds.

short *a*	short *e*	short *i*	short *o*	short *u*
man	wet	dig	hop	run

Circle the words.

man   wet   dig   hop   run

r u n a p x d i g y
j r h o p g t w e t
d k a m u w l m a n

Practice
Read, trace, and write the words.

man man

wet wet

dig dig

hop hop

run run

Gus Can Get a Pet

Review the sounds.

short *a*	short *e*	short *i*	short *o*	short *u*
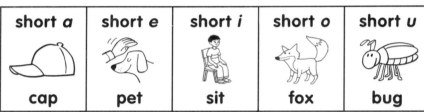				
cap	pet	sit	fox	bug

Circle the words.

cap   pet   sit   fox   bug

a w b u g z d f o x

p e t o v s i t q e

d c a p h u v f i k

Practice
Read, trace, and write the words.

cap cap

pet pet

sit sit

fox fox

bug bug

Ben Bat Is Sad

Review the sounds.

short *a*	short *e*	short *i*	short *o*	short *u*
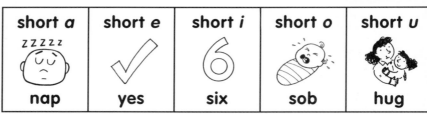				
nap	yes	six	sob	hug

Circle the words.

nap   yes   six   sob   hug

r s i x g z y e s m

s o b j t r u q e o

n a p w u t v h u g

Practice
Read, trace, and write the words.

nap nap

yes yes

six six

sob sob

hug hug

Dot's Big Red Hat

Review the sounds.

short *a*	short *e*	short *i*	short *o*	short *u*

hat	ten	in	box	mug

Circle the words.

hat	ten	in	box	mug

q i n x g t e n s m

s k h a t a z m u g

n r p w b o x h e j

Practice
Read, trace, and write the words.

hat hat

ten ten

in in

box box

mug mug

CONGRATULATIONS!

your name

You read 12 short-vowel books & completed this mini-workbook.

You are a **PHONICS STAR!**